THE WILD AND WOOLLY ANIMAL BOOK

BY NITA JONAS

PICTURES BY DALE MAXEY

RANDOM HOUSE, INC. NEW YORK

With love for Mother, Dad, Hank

and a people-dog named Happy

Library of Congress Catalog Card Number: 61-7873   *Manufactured in the United States of America*

GIRAFFE

The yellow giraffe
is tall as can be,
His lunch is a bunch
of leaves off a tree.

He has a very long neck
and his legs are long, too
And he can run faster than
his friends in the zoo.

WALRUS

The funny,
fat walrus
sits in
the sea

Where
the weather
is freezing
and cold
as can be.

His whiskers
are droopy
and his tusks
are white

And he doesn't
do much
but sit day
and night.

KANGAROO

The brown kangaroo is very funny,

She leaps and runs and hops like a bunny.

And on her stomach is a pocket so wide

Her baby can jump in and go for a ride!

SEAL

In the frozen North

lives the shiny black seal

Who pops in the water and eats

fish for his meal.

He has four floppy flippers

instead of four feet

And long droopy whiskers and

a smile

that is

sweet.

POLAR BEAR

In the cold, cold North
  where there's snow in the air
Lives the white, fuzzy,
    furry polar bear.
He's a very good swimmer
    and he thinks it's nice
To take a nap
    on a block of ice!

TIGER

"Grrrrrr" says the tiger who is very mean
With orange and black stripes and eyes of green.
He lives in the jungle and he looks like a cat
But I wouldn't want to meet a cat like that!

LEOPARD

Look out for the leopard
who leaps from a tree,

The wildest, the fiercest,
the meanest is he.

His body is orange
with lots and lots

of big black dots
called leopard spots.

REINDEER

The reindeer has antlers on his head

    And at Christmas time he pulls a sled.

He lives in the North Pole where it snows the most

    But his brown fur coat keeps him warm

                as toast.

SKUNK

The skunk has a large
    bushy tail of black

And a wide, white stripe
    running down his back.

But please don't take
    him home as a pet

For he's the smelliest
    fellow you ever met!

OTTER

The brown furry otter is playful and gay

He lives in water
and swims every day.

He slides down a mud hill
and gobbles a fish

For a fish is the otter's

favorite dish.

The fat, gray elephant
is huge in size
With big floppy ears
and two tiny eyes.
He fills his trunk with
water each hour
And sprays himself
when he takes a shower.

ELEPHANT

PENGUIN

The black and white penguin is a bird who can't fly,

He lives in the South Pole where it's cold and dry.

His bill is yellow and his flippers are wide

And he walks with a waddle from side to side.

LION

King of
the animals
is the big
yellow lion

Who can
look fierce
without even tryin'.

His mane is woolly
and he scares
birds and bees

For his roar
shakes the leaves
right down
off the trees!

PORCUPINE

The small round animal with quills on his spine

Looks like a pincushion and is called porcupine.

The sharp quills protect his body of yellow

So please don't touch this prickly fellow.

HIPPOPOTAMUS

The lazy hippopotamus has a mouth full of teeth

And a fat brown body with short legs beneath.

On his head are two tusks

that are small but strong

And he sits in the water

and eats all day long.

CAMEL

On the brown camel's back   is a very big bump

And that is called
a camel's hump.

He lives in the desert
in a very hot land

And nibbles on palm leaves
and sleeps on the sand.

MONKEY

The monkey can climb
up the tallest tree

And hang by his tail
    for he's smart as can be.

He gobbles bananas
        and chatters all day

And he's full of mischief
    in every way.

RHINOCEROS

The gray rhinoceros has a horn on his nose

And he's big and heavy from his head to his toes.

His skin is tough and when he comes near

The jungle animals tremble with fear.

FOX

The fox is smart
    and sly as can be

And a great big
    bushy tail has he.

He can run very fast,
    His fur is red,

And he lives in the woods
    in a tree-trunk bed.

PANDA

The brown panda bear
is big in size

With funny black circles
around his eyes.

His face is woolly and white
as can be

And he loves to swim
or climb a tree.

LLAMA

The llama is smaller than a camel and bigger than a goat

And on his back is a brown fur coat.

He lives in the mountains and carries heavy loads

Up and down the rocky roads.

ZEBRA

The zebra has black and white stripes, of course,

And he looks just like a little horse.

Each day in the jungle he gallops along,

For he may be small but his legs are strong.